OFF BEAT!

BY **CHLOE LEWIS**
ILLUSTRATED BY **LISA WILEY**

Walkthrough

Read this first - or turn the page to go straight to the story!

The Characters

Tash

Tash is a drummer. She wants to be in a band but she needs to find some more members!

Off Beat

Off Beat is Tash's new band. It is made up of four members: Tash, Jon, Harry and Steph.

The Rival Band

Pippa and Lily are in Tash's old band. Pippa is a singer. She does not get on with Tash. Lily plays the guitar.

Key Facts

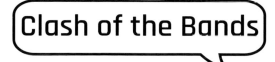
Clash of the Bands

Clash of the Bands is a big competition to pick the best band.

It's important for a band to practise lots. Then they can perform well at gigs.

Practise

Gig

Gigs are smaller shows that bands can perform at. This is where bands can show off what they can do.

Story Background

Tash is a drummer but she doesn't get on with her band's singer, Pippa. After an argument, Tash decides to start her own band. Will Tash make it to Clash of the Bands with her new band?

Pippa, Lily and Tash are practising for a big contest - Clash of the Bands!

They argue and Tash walks out.

Next day at school, Tash can hear some music.

MUSIC

They play some music together.

They ask Jon's older brother, Harry, to join.

Their first gig does not go well.

Steph joins and they name the band Off Beat.

Off Beat practise lots.

They start to sound really good!

But Tash sees Pippa and Lily arguing a lot.

Finally it is Clash of the Bands.

CLASH OF THE BANDS

Things don't go well for Pippa and Lily.

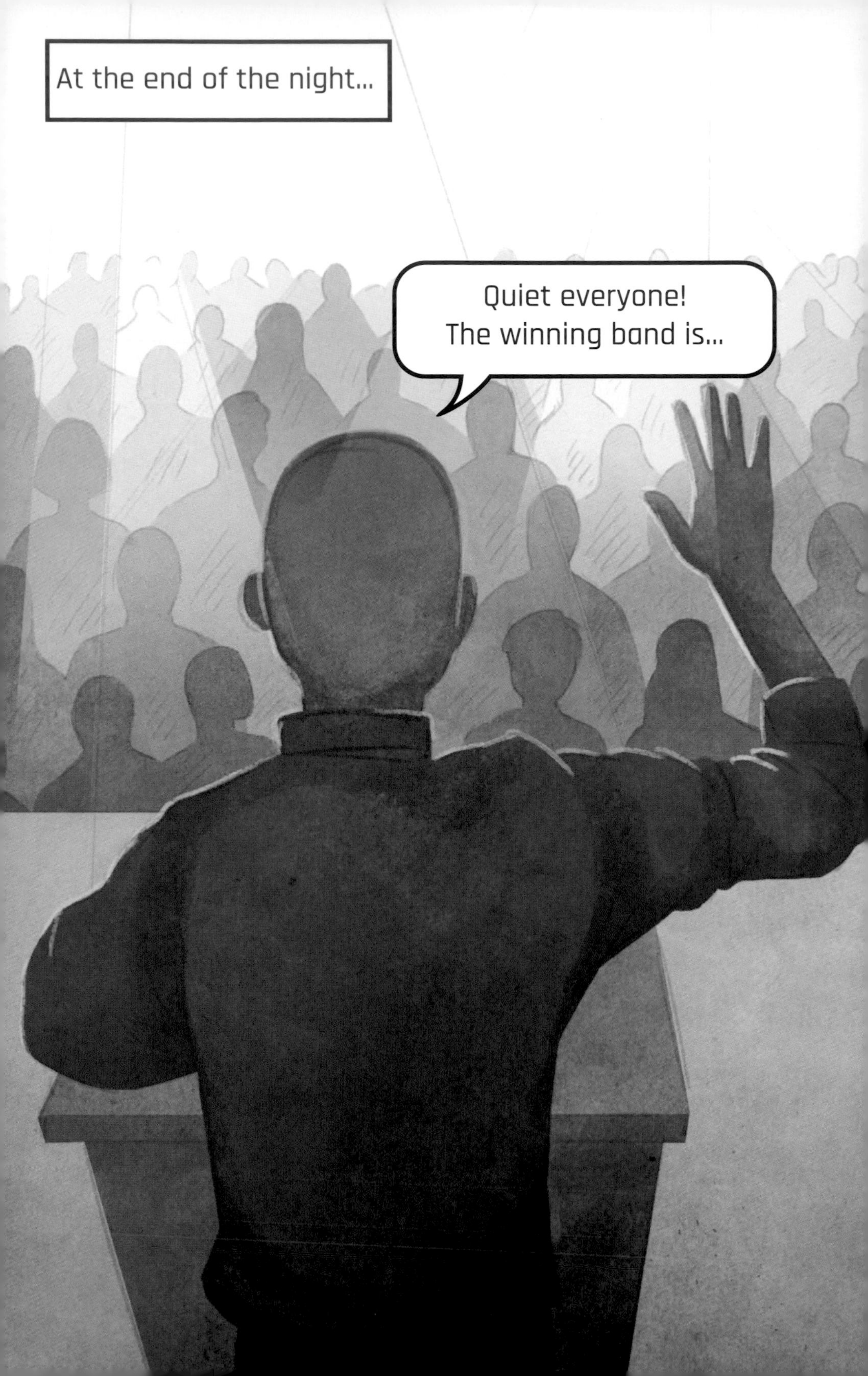
At the end of the night...
Quiet everyone! The winning band is...

Rehearsal...

Answer the questions below. Each correct answer gains you points. Are you a Rookie or a Rock Star?

1 *Multiple Choice:*
What instrument does Tash play?
a) Drums
b) Guitar
c) Keyboard

1pt

2 *Multiple Choice:*
Who is Harry?
a) Tash's dad
b) Steph's little brother
c) Jon's big brother

1pt

3 Why do Pippa and Lily not do very well?

2pts

4 *Fill in the sentence:*
Off Beat is up next. They _____!

3pts

Explore...

Think about the following:

- What do you think Off Beat will do next?

- What could Pippa have done to bring her band together? Do you think Lily will stay w...

- How do you think Tash felt ....e story?

Other Titles

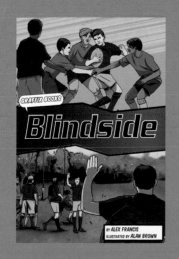

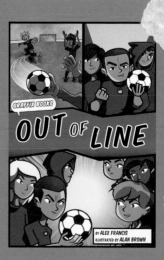

6 *Multiple Choice:*
In the end, who who wins the Clash of the Bands? **1pt**
a) Off Beat
b) Pippa and Lily
c) The Dark Void

Answers on the next page. Every correct answer earns points (pts) Which level are you?

Level:
0 - 1pts = Rookie
2 - 4pts = Backing Vocals
5 - 7pts = Guitarist
8 - 9pts = Lead Singer
10pts = Rock Star